THE POLAR EXPRESS

To Karen

Paperback and audio CD edition first published in 2017 by Andersen Press Ltd.

First published in Great Britain in 1985 by Andersen Press Ltd.,

20 Vauxhall Bridge Road, London SW1V 2SA.

Copyright © Chris Van Allsburg, 1985

The rights of Chris Van Allsburg to be identified as the author and

illustrator of this work have been asserted by him in accordance with

the Copyright, Designs and Patents Act, 1988.

All rights reserved.

Printed and bound in China.

3 5 7 9 10 8 6 4 2

British Library Cataloguing in Publication Data available.

ISBN 978 1 78344 568 4 (Paperback & CD)

ISBN 978 1 78344 640 7 (Hardback & CD)

ISBN 978 1 78344 079 5 (Hardback)

ISBN 978 1 78344 333 8 (Paperback)

THE POLAR EXPRESS

Written and Illustrated by

CHRIS VAN ALLSBURG

ANDERSEN PRESS

On Christmas Eve, many years ago, I lay quietly in my bed. I did not rustle the sheets. I breathed slowly and silently. I was listening for a sound – a sound a friend had told me I'd never hear – the ringing bells of Santa's sleigh.

"There is no Santa," my friend had insisted, but I knew he was wrong.

Late that night I did hear sounds, though not of ringing bells. From outside came the sounds of hissing steam and squeaking metal. I looked through my window and saw a train standing perfectly still in front of my house.

It was wrapped in an apron of steam. Snowflakes fell lightly around it. A conductor stood at the open door of one of the cars. He took a large pocket watch from his vest, then looked up at my window. I put on my slippers and robe. I tiptoed downstairs and out the door.

"All aboard," the conductor cried out. I ran up to him.

"Well," he said, "are you coming?"

"Where?" I asked.

"Why, to the North Pole of course," was his answer. "This is the Polar Express." I took his outstretched hand and he pulled me aboard.

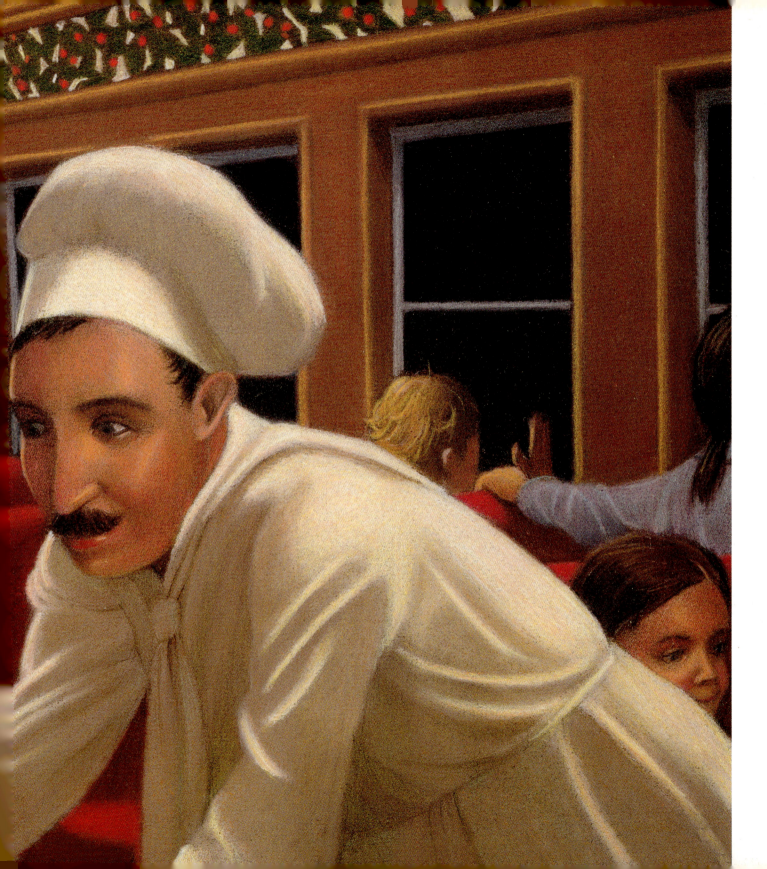

The train was filled with other children, all in their pyjamas and nightgowns. We sang Christmas carols and ate candies with nougat centres as white as snow. We drank hot cocoa as thick and rich as melted chocolate bars. Outside, the lights of towns and villages flickered in the distance as the Polar Express raced northward.

Soon there were no more
lights to be seen. We
travelled through cold, dark
forests, where lean wolves
roamed and white-tailed
rabbits hid from our train as
it thundered through the
quiet wilderness.

We climbed mountains so high it seemed as if we would scrape the moon. But the Polar Express never slowed down. Faster and faster we ran along, rolling over peaks and through valleys like a car on a roller coaster.